Psalm 119

Walking in the Light
A FLOURISH BIBLE STUDY JOURNAL

Mindy Kiker and Jenny Kochert

Welcome,

We're delighted you're here. Your presence with us signals a season of refreshing, a time to dig into the Bible and hear God speak. This **Flourish Bible Study Journal** is designed to help you grow *"like an olive tree flourishing in the house of God . . . trusting in God's unfailing love for ever and ever." Psalm 52:8*

Whatever the circumstances of your life right now, Jesus is waiting to meet you where you are with the insight you need to take the next step. A Flourish Journal invites you to create a quiet space to cultivate confidence in your life right now. As you posture yourself to hear, you will receive the Word you need to step forward into the fulfillment of the promises God has spoken.

You are going to be amazed at what you discover as you pursue the daily practices of the DECLARE Bible Study Approach. One friend likens this approach to *"Holy Spirit sunglasses"* to see through the surface into the deep waters: "I've been able to see deeper into the Bible than I've ever done before. The Holy Spirit has used DECLARE to bring much more life into my Bible time."

As you practice the DECLARE Bible Study Approach, you will be equipped to open any part of the Bible to hear Jesus speak. This journal comes from our God-breathed desire to walk with you, to take the truth you explore in Scripture and see it activated in your life.

HOW TO GET THE MOST OUT OF A FLOURISH BIBLE STUDY JOURNAL

We recommend you **Fight for Your Fifteen** by committing at least 15 minutes a day to this study. *"Commit to the Lord whatever you do, and he will establish your plans." (Proverbs 16:3)*

This Journal is designed to be completed in 20-days, one month at five days per week. But feel free to take longer or shorter depending on the time you have available. Each week is organized around a Declaration Verse which guides the five stages of the DECLARE Bible Study Approach: Read & Write, Investigate, Imagine, Listen, and Declare.

Each day, three levels of study are offered depending on the time you have available:

 Today's DECLARE Practice
(can be completed in 10-15 minutes)

 Have a Little More Time?
(another 10-15 minutes)

 Digging Deeper
(another 10-15 minutes)

If you're strapped for time, just do **Today's DECLARE Practice** and skip **Have a Little More Time?** and **Digging Deeper**. No guilt. No pressure. Take each day as it comes, with your goal to *Fight for Your Fifteen*. Sometimes fifteen minutes is all you have and you won't make it past the first level.

If you have a medium amount of time, do the first two levels that day. If you have plenty of time, and the topic is intriguing, do all three levels. But take each day as it comes.

Now, we know that some of you are going to hate leaving blank spaces in your journal, and if you fall too far behind, you'll give up and stop altogether. We created these three levels with our less-is-more approach focusing on one Declaration Verse each week is to help you keep going. You're trying to develop your Bible Study muscles. Strength is built through daily consistency, not a huge burst of weightlifting and then nothing for days.

Please resist the Accuser who says you're doing a terrible job if you just do **Today's DECLARE Practice** and skip the other two levels. The study is designed with this flexibility to meet you in any season of life. A little bit is better than none.

The **Digging Deeper** part provides an optional reading plan. Notice the word "optional." Don't make it mandatory if you don't have time. We created this Bible Study Journal with our simple approach to Bible Study so you can go deep into a small portion of Scripture to explore God's Word.

Choosing a Flourish Bible Study Journal is a great first step to strengthening your spiritual muscles a little bit each day. We know you'll grow as you:

1. **Get curious about the Word.** What does the Word say about your situation? What does it say about God himself? About your family? About the future? As you learn more about the Bible, how to study it, and how to dig deeper, you will become hungry to get into the Word.

2. **Get to Know Jesus.** Jesus is the Word personified. He embodies everything God desires to reveal to us. John tells us that *"the Word became flesh and dwelt among us." John 1:14 (ESV)* That's Jesus! His love and obedience crushed the power of death. By getting to know God in three persons, we come to understand the whole Bible in terms of God's plan to rescue all of humanity–this includes you and me, right here, right now, today.

3. **Seek for a personal word.** When trying to gain understanding, we look for answers in several places. You may reach out to trusted leaders in your life. It is good to seek wisdom in a multitude of counsel, but then you must draw away to a quiet place and seek God yourself with this prayer: *Father, I have sought much advice, and now I want to know what You have to say about this situation.* When we pursue Jesus, and the inevitable storms come, His promises hold us fast.

This is how you flourish in faith, family and life. You dig into the Bible, fasten your eyes on Holy Spirit, and wait until you receive a personal word. The DECLARE Bible Study Approach brings all these elements together as you dig into the Bible and hear Jesus speak.

A Note to Group Leaders

We are pleased you have chosen to gather a group of ladies to enjoy this Flourish Bible Study together. The study is designed to create deep, thoughtful conversations. Chatting through the insights gained using the five simple DECLARE practices each week will guide the discussion to reveal personal a-ha's that come straight from Scripture. It is motivating and encouraging when ladies share how God speaks in their lives.

We have provided here a few considerations regarding scheduling:

† Since it is a four-week study, you have several choices for your meeting schedule. You can meet up weekly for four weeks, or maybe you meet only twice and cover two weeks at a time. Most groups enjoy 1-1/2 or 2 hours together.

† Some groups like to add a fifth meeting time to gather before the study begins to hand out the books.

We suggest that you make use of the weekly **Discussion Topics** located at the end of each week to facilitate the discussion. Most facilitators like to use this guide as a building block to create a general time schedule for your meeting. You may want to reserve fifteen minutes or so at the end of your group time to share prayer requests.

Gathering women to share their stories invites God's love to shine: *"They triumphed over him by the blood of the Lamb and by the word of their testimony."* (Revelation 12:11) We pray that you are blessed as you flourish together!

Table of Contents

Reading Plan & Weekly Scripture Declaration

Week 1

Declaration Verse:
Psalm 119:105

"Your word is a lamp for my feet, a light on my path."

Digging Deeper Reading Plan:
Psalm 119:1-40

Week 2

Declaration Verse:
Psalm 119:114

"You are my refuge and my shield; I have put my hope in your word." (ESV)

Digging Deeper Reading Plan:
Psalm 119:41-88

Week 3

Declaration Verse:
Psalm 119:130

"The unfolding of your words gives light; it gives understanding to the simple."

Digging Deeper Reading Plan:
Psalm 119:89-136

Week 4

Declaration Verse:
Psalm 119:165

"Great peace have those who love your law, and nothing can make them stumble."

Digging Deeper Reading Plan:
Psalm 119:137-176

Declare Bible Study Approach

*"We know that the Son of God has come
and has given us understanding, so that
we may know him who is true. . . ."*

1 John 5:20

The Declare Bible Study Approach equips us to dig deeper into a passage of Scripture in order to know God's Word intimately and apply it to our lives. *(1 Corinthians 2:10-15)* When His Word is activated in our midst, new life is released, and we will begin to flourish where we are planted.

Learn more about the DECLARE Bible Study Approach and how to use online Bible study aids. Log onto **www.flourishgathering.com/declare** to view our video series.

Engage Prayer Method

The DECLARE Bible Study Approach begins by engaging or tuning your ears and heart to God's voice. The ENGAGE Prayer Method prepares your heart and mind to hear:

TOSS: Throw your cares on God. Let Him bear your burdens. *Psalm 55:22*

CATCH: Receive the peace that surpasses all understanding. *Philippians 4:7*

INVITE: Take every thought captive. Invite clarity and focus. Refuse confusion, distraction, or double-mindedness. *2 Corinthians 10:5*

OPEN: Ask God if you have turned away or closed your heart to anyone. Release the offense, open your heart, and give the situation into God's care. *Psalm 139:23*

EXPECT: Tell God that you are looking forward to hearing from Him. Let the excitement of time in His presence build expectation in your heart. *Habakkuk 2:1*

STAGE 1: *Read & Write* 📖

Start with a Bible verse or short passage you want to explore further. We call this the Declaration Verse which is your focus for the following activities:

† Read the Declaration Verse slowly once or twice, out loud if you are able.

† Write the verse in your journal, including the verses before and after.

† Read the entire chapter for context.

† Read the Declaration Verse in another Bible translation.

STAGE 2: *Investigate* 🔍

After reading the Declaration Verse and corresponding chapter, look deeper into the Scriptures. Investigate as little or as much as time allows. Online resources like BibleGateway.com or BlueLetterBible.org will help:

† Highlight words in the Declaration Verse you want to research more. We teach you how to do a word study to gain greater insight into the passage.

† Read cross references which are other verses with a similar message to help you better understand a verse, word, or principle.

† Read a Bible commentary.

STAGE 3: *Imagine*

Read the Declaration Verse and insert yourself in the story. Use your imagination to be present in the scene. Ask yourself the following questions:

† When and where is this taking place?

† Who is speaking? About what? Why?

† What characteristics of God are revealed in this passage?

† What promises of God are revealed in this passage?

STAGE 4: *Listen*

Invite the Word to speak personally into your mind and heart by asking these questions:

† How does this passage of Scripture apply to me?

† Is there anything I need to receive or surrender in my life?

† Lord, how I can apply Your Word to the frustrations, disappointments, fears, or hurts in my life?

Listening can be pursued for several days. God may speak unexpectedly any time of day or night as His revelation is released to you.

STAGE 5: *Declare* 🎤

Write a declaration of what you received as you meditated on the Word. This can be a statement of God's promise to you, an affirmation of the healing He has given you, or a proclamation of truth. A declaration may include Scripture, your own words, or some of each.

Walking in the Light

As we prayed over this study, a favorite children's song came to mind: *This little light of mine; I'm gonna let it shine.*

We all want to shine for God's glory, don't we?

Most of us strategize to keep shining by making sure that life is characterized by blessing, joy, freedom, grace, and strength. We focus all our energy to stay on high paths to circle the bright and shining mountain peaks.

We strenuously avoid any path that leads down into the dark, gloomy valleys—places that call for obedience, submission, weakness, patience, and heaven-forbid, suffering. We fanatically pursue our relationship with God to stay at the top of the sun-kissed peaks, never to descend into the shadowy depths below.

We construct zip lines and catapults to transport us from one peak to the next, circumventing paths that lead down the mountain side into the dark valley recesses. It looks frightening down there in the gorges.

Despite our determined attempts to control our circumstances, some paths start to dip down, dangerously low. Fear pushes us to kick our spiritual disciplines into high gear:

more time in the Word, fasting, praying, church attendance. Work. Harder. Must. Not. Succumb. To. Suffering.

When I finally slip and find myself stuck in a crevasse, I moan piteously and cry out like the psalmist David, "Where are you God? Why have you abandoned me?"

You know what He says?

"I am here in this place with you. The valleys are part of My blessing too."

"Blessing?!" I protest, "This is not the reward I signed up for. Don't you see me working like crazy? I don't deserve this!"

God replies, "This is my good plan for you."

Good plan? Really? This?

But you know what I've discovered?

He's right.

Valleys are vital to our growth and strength, just like the mountain peaks, but not as attractive. Valleys are the way to the top. In the dark valley, God's light shines more brightly. Here we learn to persevere. We are strengthened by trials. We cling to the Word of God as if life depends on it.

During trials, the promises of God take on a sweetness that is seldom tasted any other way. Through the Scriptures, Holy Spirit gathers us in His embrace and comforts us with supernatural joy and peace. Jesus joins us in the middle of the storm and creates calm in our hearts. Father God walks with us in the still of the morning and whispers reassurances to an anguished soul.

The promises of God sustain us through all seasons of life: joy and grief, celebration and mourning, work and rest. **The Word itself becomes nourishment for our journey.** We cannot survive without it.

What does the Bible say about the sustaining qualities of God's Word? Right smack dab in the middle of the Scriptures is this lengthy psalm that is wholly dedicated to glorifying God and His Word. You know, the longest chapter in the Bible. The one with a record *one hundred seventy-six* verses. Yes, the one and only Psalm 119.

Nearly every verse in this remarkable chapter refers lovingly to the Word of God using terms such as testimonies, precept, law, righteousness, judgments, commandments, way and statutes.

Psalm 119 stirs our souls to marvel at the majesty of the Word. This inspiring chapter is a burst of color and brilliance in the landscape of Scripture: "In the kaleidoscope you look once, and there is a strangely beautiful form. You shift the glass a very little, and another shape, equally delicate and beautiful, is before your eyes. So it is here." (Spurgeon's Commentary on the Bible, Psalm 119)

The psalmist demonstrates in 176 different ways how the power of Scripture reaches into every circumstance of life, every bright mountain top, and every shadowy valley. The Lord's promises never leave us, never forsake us.

As we feast on Psalm 119, we pray you will experience the light of God's Word.

Guided by the Word

DECLARATION VERSE

"Your word is a lamp for my feet,
a light on my path." Psalm 119:105

A Lamp for My Feet

If you're not a morning person, this may be challenging, but give it try. Think back to the last time you arose before dawn. Close your eyes and remember the sounds and sights.

The earth, silent and thick with slumber, turns slowly toward the sun. At last, the sky brightens with dramatic colors. Silence gives way to bird songs announcing the day's arrival, full of mercies that are new every morning.

But what if you dread the arrival of a new day?

When you're in a season of waiting or enduring, days drag on with little hope of change or improvement. At these times, our prayers may be filled with accusations and complaints more than praise and gratitude. Favorite Bible verses may sound mocking more than comforting.

Heaven help the person who belts out, *"This is the day that the LORD has made; let us rejoice and be glad in it." Psalm 118:24 (ESV)*

And yet, this is truth. Choosing words of joy shifts our attitude. When we keep our eyes on God, and not on our circumstances, we begin to see possibilities where none existed before. We begin to feel hope.

If we know this is true, then why do we struggle to choose the light of gladness? Why do we languish in the darkness of despair, apathetic to reach out for help? We need a light that shines even when we are unable to turn it on for ourselves.

The psalmist declares that God's Word is such a light source: *"Your word is a lamp for my feet, a light on my path." Psalm 119:105*

The Bible overflows with promises of the glorious path we walk when we choose to follow our God. Verse after verse proclaims victory and freedom. As Christ-followers, we are described as overcomers, complete with sword and shield, feet that do not slip, soaring on wings like eagles.

Let's look again as the Word shines on our path. God does promise a glorious path, but it is not one of ease and comfort. The Bible acknowledges that our path will take us into challenging terrain.

When Jesus urges us to take up our cross and follow Him, I shudder. When David describes the valley of the shadow of death, I tremble. When Job scrapes his ravaged skin with shards of pottery, I recoil.

I find both stories of suffering and stories of overcoming in the Bible. **As I ponder these stories, I'm surprised to discover both suffering and overcoming as part of every story.** The men and women who walked with God experience the full gamut: sorrow and glory, tears and laughter, birth and death.

And it appears that grief leads to glory. Death leads to life. Weakness leads to strength. This is the upside-down Kingdom of God. Sorrow is not a dead end; instead, it is a thoroughfare to a place of rejoicing. Tears turn to shouts of joy. Sadness descends, but rejoicing comes in the morning. We believe in a God who transforms all circumstances into good for those who love Him. (Romans 8:28)

For those who love Him.

Maybe we walk on a God-lighted path by loving Him first and **choosing His Word to be the lamp that illuminates our way.** When I read through the Scriptures, one of my favorite personal reflections is to ask, *"What if I don't do that? What if I don't choose God's Word as the light for my path? What if I don't love Him first?"*

Because I have a free will, I can choose other guiding lights. I can choose to lavish my worship elsewhere.

Throughout the Old Testament, God confronts our love of idols. When Moses returns from a 40-day excursion on Mount Sinai, he finds the Israelites worshiping a golden calf. (Exodus 32) Hadn't they just been freed from Egypt and sustained in the wilderness by miracle after miracle? How quickly they abandoned their first love. Although they promise to be faithful to their God, they repeatedly fail to keep Him first in their hearts.

We are no different. Every day we are tempted to choose a different lamp for our feet, another light for our path. How to choose well? We don't want to trudge along for months or years, unaware that we have followed a false guide.

Let Psalm 119 ignite your desire to dig deep into God's Word that it may delight your thoughts and captivate your affections. Meditate on His promises day and night. Obey His commandments. Seek understanding and wisdom. Don't be satisfied with anything less.

Nothing in all the world compares with our God. Many other false gods sparkle with counterfeit illumination. These substitute saviors vie for our attention, but *their light does not sustain.*

When you consistently spend time in the Word, enjoying time with the Lord, you familiarize yourself with the true light. Then when false lights shimmer and gleam, you recognize them as imitations. You will not be tempted, but instead, you will worship only your first love.

May your confidence in God's Word grow and your love for His precepts flourish as you walk in His light.

Engage Prayer Method

The DECLARE Bible Study Approach begins by engaging or tuning your ears and heart to God's voice. The ENGAGE Prayer Method prepares your heart and mind to hear:

TOSS: Throw your cares on God. Let Him bear your burdens. *Psalm 55:22*

CATCH: Receive the peace that surpasses all understanding. *Philippians 4:7*

INVITE: Take every thought captive. Invite clarity and focus. Refuse confusion, distraction, or double-mindedness. *2 Corinthians 10:5*

OPEN: Ask God if you have turned away or closed your heart to anyone. Release the offense, open your heart, and give the situation into God's care. *Psalm 139:23*

EXPECT: Tell God that you are looking forward to hearing from Him. Let the excitement of time in His presence build expectation in your heart. *Habakkuk 2:1*

Guided by the Word

DAY ONE

Declaration Verse
"Your word is a lamp for my feet,
a light on my path."
Psalm 119:105

TODAY'S DECLARE PRACTICE *Read & Write*

[ ] Read Psalm 119:105 slowly once or twice, out loud if you are able.

[ ] Write Psalm 119:104-106 in the space below. *Feel free to get creative!*

HAVE A LITTLE MORE TIME?

[ ] Read Psalm chapters 118 and 120 for context.
Write out a few observations.

_____

_____

_____

_____

_____

_____

_____

_____

_____

[ ] Read Psalm 119:105 in another Bible translation.
Make note of the similarities and differences you see.

_____

_____

_____

_____

_____

_____

_____

_____

_____

_____

🌱 DIGGING DEEPER: PSALM 119:1-8

[ ] Read Psalm 119:1-8

[ ] Read and Write

Write any verse that stands out to you.

_____

_____

_____

_____

_____

[ ] Write any general thoughts or questions you have as you
read the passage today.

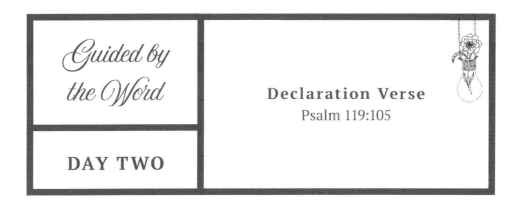

Guided by the Word

DAY TWO

Declaration Verse
Psalm 119:105

TODAY'S DECLARE PRACTICE *Investigate*

Today we begin looking deeper into the Declaration Verse. Investigate as little or as much as time allows. Online resources like BibleGateway.com or BlueLetterBible.org will help you during your investigation.

[ ] Conduct a Word Study: Part One

Read the Declaration Verse and highlight any words you want to research more. Write these words below.

_____

_____

_____

_____

_____

_____

_____

_____

_____

[ ] Conduct a Word Study: Part Two

Want to learn more about the DECLARE Bible Study
Approach and how to do a word study? Log onto
www.flourishgathering.com/declare to view our
video series.

Using BlueLetterBible.org or another online resource,
choose a word from the Declaration Verse and conduct a
word study. This is as simple as looking up the original
Greek or Hebrew word, reading the definitions of that word,
and looking at how it is used in other verses in the Bible.

Record the results of your word study here.

_____

_____

_____

_____

_____

HAVE A LITTLE MORE TIME?

[ ] Read these cross references for Psalm 119:105:

    †   Psalm 19:8

    †   Proverbs 6:23

    †   Ephesians 5:13

Reading cross references will help you better understand a verse, word, or principle. What did you discover? Write your insights.

_____

_____

_____

_____

_____

_____

_____

_____

_____

[ ] Read a commentary. A commentary is a collection of
explanatory notes written by a Bible scholar to help us
understand the Scriptures. Find these online. A good place
to begin is Matthew Henry, C.H. Spurgeon, or David Guzik.

Write your observations, quotes, or notes.

DIGGING DEEPER: PSALM 119:9-16

[ ] Read Psalm 119:9-16

[ ] Investigate

Highlight a couple of key words that stand out to you in
the verses you read. Using BlueLetterBible.org look up
the Greek or Hebrew word and definition of one of those
words. Write your findings below.

[ ] Write any general thoughts or questions you have as you read the verses today.

Declaration Verse
Psalm 119:105

DAY THREE

 TODAY'S DECLARE PRACTICE *Imagine*

> *Remember to ENGAGE as you prepare to imagine: toss, catch, invite, open, expect. Invite the Word to speak personally into your mind and heart.*

[ ] Read Psalm 119:105

You may want to read different translations. We suggest you scout around in your Bible for any notes or perhaps an introduction to the Psalms or specifically Psalm 119. When using your imagination, it helps to keep in mind the context of the chapter and book that you're in. Insert yourself in the scene as you ponder the following questions. Use your imagination and all your senses to be present in the words of Scripture.

[ ] When and where is this taking place? What do you
     imagine you might see, hear, touch, taste, or smell?

_____

_____

_____

_____

_____

_____

_____

_____

[ ] Who is speaking or writing? Who are they addressing?
     Others? God? Themselves?

_____

_____

_____

_____

_____

[ ] What are they speaking or writing about?
    What is their purpose?

_____

_____

_____

_____

_____

_____

 ## HAVE A LITTLE MORE TIME?

[ ] What characteristics of God are revealed in the
Declaration Verse?

Is He steadfast, faithful, just, trustworthy, nurturing,
kind, gentle, or strong? What do you see revealed about
His nature in this passage of Scripture?

_____

_____

_____

_____

_____

_____

[ ] What promises of God are revealed in the Declaration Verse?

Write any observations, key words, or questions you have
as you ponder the Declaration Verse. If you have time, you
may want to do another word study.

DIGGING DEEPER: PSALM 119:17-24

[ ] Read Psalm 119:17-24

[ ] Imagine

Place yourself in the Scriptures as you ponder the following questions. What is happening? Imagine that you are there. What do you notice?

[ ] Write any general thoughts or questions you have as you
    read the verses today.

Declaration Verse
Psalm 119:105

 TODAY'S DECLARE PRACTICE *Listen*

> *Remember to ENGAGE as you prepare to listen: toss, catch, invite, open, expect. Invite the Word to speak personally into your mind and heart. God's voice will never accuse you. He may bring gentle conviction which can cause grief, but God always brings hope.*

Listening can be pursued for several days. God may speak unexpectedly at random times of day or night as His revelation is released to you. Ask this question as you listen to God's voice.

[ ] How does these truth apply to me? What do you want me to see, God?

_____

_____

_____

_____

_____

_____

_____

_____

_____

 HAVE A LITTLE MORE TIME?

[ ] Ponder and pray: how I can apply these truths to the
frustrations, disappointments, fears, or hurts in my life?
Is there anything I need to surrender or receive in my life?

_____

_____

_____

_____

_____

_____

_____

_____

_____

_____

_____

🌱 DIGGING DEEPER: PSALM 119:25-32

[ ] Read Psalm 119:25-32

[ ] Listen

Ask yourself: how do the truths I find in these verses apply to me? What does God want to speak to me?

_____

_____

_____

_____

_____

_____

_____

[ ] Write any general thoughts or questions you have as you
   read this passage.

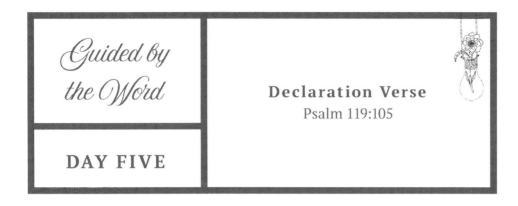

Guided by the Word

DAY FIVE

Declaration Verse
Psalm 119:105

TODAY'S DECLARE PRACTICE *Declare*

Write a declaration of what you received as you meditated
on the Word. This can be a statement of God's promise to
you, an affirmation of the healing He has given you, or a
proclamation of a truth He revealed. A declaration may
include Scripture, your own words, or some of each.

_____

_____

_____

_____

_____

DIGGING DEEPER: PSALM 119:33-40

[ ] Read Psalm 119:33-40

[ ] Write any notes or observations you made from these verses.
    Is there one verse that stands out to you?

[ ] How does this passage inspire you to walk in the light?

REFLECT ON YOUR WEEK 📅

Write out Psalm 119:105 by hand if you memorized it or
summarize the Declaration Verse in your own words below.

Spend a few minutes documenting your insights,
"a-ha" moments, and revelations from this week of
digging into the Bible.

Week One: Discussion Topics

We provide discussion topics to help facilitate conversations with friends as you enjoy this study together, or you can ponder these questions as a personal reflection. Even if you are not able to meet up with others, you're invited to join us in our private Facebook Group at facebook.com/groups/flourishgathering/

1. Do you have any thoughts or reactions to this week's devotional? Here are two passages from *A Lamp for My Feet* to inspire conversation:

   "When you're in a season of waiting or enduring, days drag on with little hope of change or improvement. At such times, our prayers may be filled with accusations and complaints more than praise and gratitude. Favorite Bible verses may sound more mocking than comforting." (page 17)

   "And it appears that grief leads to glory. Death leads to life. Weakness leads to strength. This is the upside-down Kingdom of God.

Sorrow is not a dead end; instead, it is a thoroughfare to a place of rejoicing. Tears turn to shouts of joy. Sadness descends, but rejoicing comes in the morning. We believe in a God who transforms all circumstances into good for those who love Him. (Romans 8:28)" (page 19)

2. Was there a special insight you gained from the **Investigate** practice? Perhaps an interesting word study, cross reference, or commentary?

3. What happened when you used your **Imagination**? What did you discover about the context of this chapter or book of the Bible? If you had time, did you gain insight into the character or promises of God?

4. Did God speak something special you would like to share as you **Listened**?

5. What is your **Declaration**? How can we pray for you in this regard?

6. How about the Psalm 119 **Digging Deeper** reading plan? Anything interesting there?

7. How can we support one another this week? Prayer requests? Praise reports?

Notes

WEEK TWO

Hope in the Word

DECLARATION VERSE

"You are my refuge and my shield; I have put my hope in your word." Psalm 119:114 (ESV)

.

The Hiding Place

I recently purchased a new camera. As I was playing around with it, snapping pictures here and there, I snapped a picture of our dog, Chester. As I looked at the picture, my first thought was, *"Wow, I captured his personality perfectly."*

You see, others looking at the picture wouldn't necessarily notice what I perceive because they don't know him the way I do.

They wouldn't know that he loves to eat plastic and lie on our bed. He howls when he's scared and always invites all sixty pounds of himself to sit on our laps. They wouldn't know that he cries when we leave and loves to steal his sister's toys. If you don't watch him, he will eat your food, dig through your garbage, and chase the neighborhood cat.

Yet, **when I see him**, I see his unconditional love for us because, although he's a dog, I believe he knows where he came from and who rescued him. We call him our "clearance puppy" because after thirty days at the local animal shelter no one wanted him, and they dropped his adoption fee to a whopping $15. He was a shy, timid, scared little soul **hiding** in the back of his crate.

After much thought one Saturday afternoon, we adopted him on a wish and a prayer that with lots of love and a good meal, we could break through his timid shell. We hoped there would be a dog inside who would love warm hugs and a good juicy bone.

There are some who feel like Chester did those days at the shelter. They are in hiding, spiritually speaking, and they feel alone, unwanted, and unworthy of love. They are waiting for someone to love them, to want them, and make them feel worthy. ***They are longing for someone or something to let them out of their hiding place.*** We have a loving Father, a heavenly Father, who is pacing the halls of our sheltered lives, searching for hearts to respond to His love, ***a lavish love that fills every space of our broken souls*** more completely than anyone or anything else can fill.

He offers us unwavering love. No matter how many times we dig that hole, or steal that toy, He will treasure us just the same. Although I am blessed by the love, tenderness, and loyalty of what many refer to as "man's best friend," it will never compare to the love our God desires to lavish on us every day.

> *"You are my hiding place and my shield; I hope in your word."*
> Psalm 119: 114(ESV)

Not too many years ago, I sat brokenhearted, ***hiding*** inside the shell of a wounded heart. ***Today I stand rescued by the lavish love poured out on a cross two thousand years ago***, and I cannot help but respond to my Rescuer and Redeemer with love, adoration and loyalty. What I can muster up to give back will never compare to what is freely given to me.

You see, I know where I came from, and I know Who rescued me, and I will never leave His side because I was created to be loved by Him and to receive love from Him. Just like I know Chester in ways that others don't, ***God knows you in ways no one else ever will because He created you.*** He sees your unique personality, your strengths, weaknesses, giftings and struggles. He knows all your stories, and He loves you just the same.

Be reminded and encouraged today that no matter where you are in your journey of life, the safest place for you to hide is ***in Him***, and the safest place for you to place your hope, is in ***His Word***.

Engage Prayer Method

The DECLARE Bible Study Approach begins by engaging or tuning your ears and heart to God's voice. The ENGAGE Prayer Method prepares your heart and mind to hear:

TOSS: Throw your cares on God. Let Him bear your burdens. *Psalm 55:22*

CATCH: Receive the peace that surpasses all understanding. *Philippians 4:7*

INVITE: Take every thought captive. Invite clarity and focus. Refuse confusion, distraction, or double-mindedness. *2 Corinthians 10:5*

OPEN: Ask God if you have turned away or closed your heart to anyone. Release the offense, open your heart, and give the situation into God's care. *Psalm 139:23*

EXPECT: Tell God that you are looking forward to hearing from Him. Let the excitement of time in His presence build expectation in your heart. *Habakkuk 2:1*

Hope in the Word

DAY ONE

Declaration Verse
"You are my refuge and my shield;
I have put my hope in your word."
Psalm 119:114 (ESV)

 **TODAY'S DECLARE PRACTICE** *Read & Write*

[ ] Read Psalm 119:114 slowly once or twice, out loud if you
    are able.

[ ] Write Psalm 119:113-115 in the space below. *Feel free to
    get creative!*

_____

_____

_____

_____

_____

_____

HAVE A LITTLE MORE TIME?

[ ] Read Psalm chapters 117 and 121 for context. Write out a few observations.

_____

_____

_____

_____

_____

_____

[ ] Read Psalm 119:114 in another Bible translation. Make note of the similarities and differences you see.

_____

_____

_____

_____

_____

_____

DIGGING DEEPER: PSALM 119:41-50

[ ] Read Psalm 119:41-50

[ ] Read and Write

Write any verse that stands out to you as you read these verses.

_____

_____

_____

_____

_____

[ ] Write any general thoughts or questions you have as you
    read this passage.

_____

_____

_____

_____

_____

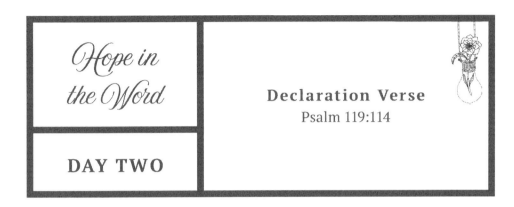

Hope in the Word

DAY TWO

Declaration Verse
Psalm 119:114

TODAY'S DECLARE PRACTICE *Investigate*

Today we begin looking deeper into the Declaration Verse. Investigate as little or as much as time allows. Online resources like BibleGateway.com or BlueLetterBible.org will help you during your investigation.

[ ] Conduct a Word Study: Part One

Read the Declaration Verse and highlight any words you want to research more. Write these words below.

_____

_____

_____

[ ] Conduct a Word Study: Part Two

Using BlueLetterBible.org or another online resource,
choose a word you selected above to conduct your word
study. This is as simple as looking up the original Greek
or Hebrew word, reading the definitions of that word, and
looking at how it is used in other verses in the Bible.

Record the results of your word study here.

HAVE A LITTLE MORE TIME?

[ ] Read any of the following cross references for Psalm 119:114:

†   Psalm 32:7

†   Hebrews 6:19

†   Romans 5:5

Reading cross references will help you better understand a verse, word, or principle.

What did you discover? Write your insights:

_____

_____

_____

_____

_____

_____

_____

[ ] Read a commentary. A commentary is a collection of explanatory notes written by a Bible scholar to help us understand the Scriptures. You can find these online. A good place to begin is Matthew Henry, C.H. Spurgeon, or David Guzik.

Write any observations, quotes, or notes.

_____

_____

_____

_____

_____

_____

_____

DIGGING DEEPER: PSALM 119:51-60

[ ] Read Psalm 119:51-60

[ ] Investigate

Highlight a couple of key words that stand out to you in the verses you read. Using BlueLetterBible.org look up the Greek or Hebrew word and definition of one of those words.

Write your findings below.

_____

_____

_____

[ ] Write any general thoughts or questions you have as you
    read the verses today.

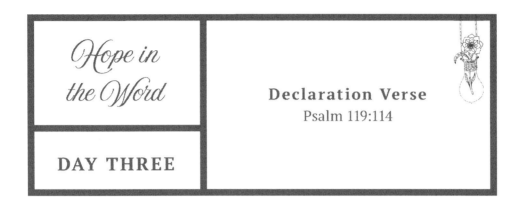

Hope in the Word

DAY THREE

Declaration Verse
Psalm 119:114

TODAY'S DECLARE PRACTICE *Imagine*

> *Remember to ENGAGE as you prepare to imagine: toss, catch, invite, open, expect. Invite the Word to speak personally into your mind and heart.*

[ ] Read Psalm 119:114.

Use your imagination and all your senses to be present in the scene.

[ ] What do a refuge and shield provide? Why do I need them?

[ ] How do I protect myself or "take refuge" when I am
     threatened –outbursts, silence, numbing distractions
     or addictions?

[ ] What would change if God's Word was my shield?

HAVE A LITTLE MORE TIME?

[ ] What characteristics of God are revealed in the
Declaration Verse?

Is He steadfast, faithful, just, trustworthy, nurturing, kind,
gentle, or strong? What do you see revealed about His nature
in this passage of Scripture?

_____

_____

_____

_____

_____

_____

_____

_____

[ ] What promises of God are revealed in the Declaration
Verse?

Write any observations, key words, or questions you have
as you ponder the Declaration Verse. If you have time, you
may want to do another word study.

_____

_____

_____

_____

_____

_____

_____

DIGGING DEEPER: PSALM 119:61-70

[ ] Read Psalm 119:61-70

[ ] Imagine

Imagine yourself in the scene as you ponder the following
questions. What is happening? Imagine you are there.
What do you notice?

_____

_____

_____

_____

_____

[ ] Write any general thoughts or questions you have as you
    read the verses today.

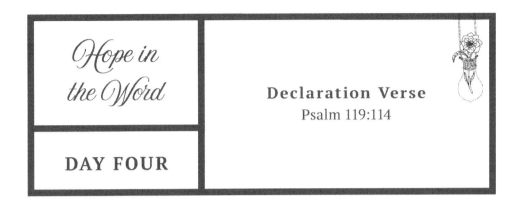

Hope in the Word

DAY FOUR

Declaration Verse
Psalm 119:114

 TODAY'S DECLARE PRACTICE *Listen*

> *Remember to ENGAGE as you prepare to listen: toss, catch, invite, open, expect. Invite the Word to speak personally into your mind and heart. God's voice will never accuse you. He may bring gentle conviction which can cause grief, but God always brings hope.*

Listening can be pursued for several days. God may speak unexpectedly at random times of day or night as His revelation is released to you. Ask this question as you listen to God's voice:

[ ] How does this verse shine the light in my life?

_____

_____

_____

_____

_____

_____

_____

_____

_____

_____

_____

_____

HAVE A LITTLE MORE TIME?

[ ] Ponder and pray: God, please show me how I protect
    myself in times of conflict. Is your Word strong enough to
    protect me instead? Am I safe to hope in you?

_____

_____

_____

_____

_____

_____

_____

_____

_____

_____

_____

🌱 DIGGING DEEPER: PSALM 119:71-80

[ ] Read Psalm 119:71-80

[ ] Listen

Ask yourself: how does this reading in Psalm 119 apply to me? Does God want to speak to my heart today through these truths?

_____

_____

_____

_____

_____

_____

_____

_____

_____

_____

[ ] Write any general thoughts or questions you have as you
read the verses today.

_____

_____

_____

_____

_____

_____

_____

_____

_____

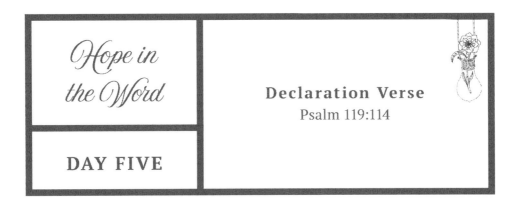

Hope in the Word

DAY FIVE

Declaration Verse
Psalm 119:114

 TODAY'S DECLARE PRACTICE *Declare*

Write out a declaration of what you received as you
meditated on the Word. This can be a statement of God's
promise to you, an affirmation of the healing He has
given you, or a proclamation of a truth. A declaration may
include Scripture, your own words, or some of each.

DIGGING DEEPER: PSALM 119:81-88

[ ] Read Psalm 119:81-88

[ ] Write any notes or observations you made from this passage. Is there one verse that stands out to you?

_____

_____

_____

_____

[ ] How does this passage inspire you to walk in the light?

_____

_____

_____

_____

_____

_____

REFLECT ON YOUR WEEK 📅

Write out Psalm 119:114 by hand if you memorized it or summarize the Declaration Verse in your own words below.

Spend a few minutes documenting your insights, "a-ha" moments, and revelations from this week of digging into the Bible.

Week Two: Discussion Topics

We provide discussion topics to help facilitate conversations with friends as you enjoy this study together, or you can ponder these questions as a personal reflection. Even if you are not able to meet up with others, you're invited to join us in our private Facebook Group at facebook.com/groups/flourishgathering/

1. Do you have any thoughts or reactions to this week's devotional? Here are two passages from *The Hiding Place* to inspire conversation:

   "There are some who feel like Chester did those days at the shelter. They are in hiding, spiritually speaking, and they feel alone, unwanted, and unworthy of love. They are waiting for someone or something to love them, to want them, and to make them feel worthy. They are longing for someone or something to let them out of their hiding place." (page 54)

   "God knows you in ways no one else ever will because He created you. He sees your unique personality, your strengths, weaknesses, giftings and struggles. He knows all your stories, and He loves you just the same." (page 55)

2. Was there a special insight you gained from the
    Investigate practice? Perhaps an interesting
    word study, cross reference, or commentary?

3. What happened when you used your **Imagination**?
    What did you discover about the context of this
    chapter or book of the Bible? If you had time,
    did you gain insight into the character or promises
    of God?

4. Did God speak something special that you would
    like to share as you **Listened**?

5. What is your **Declaration**? How can we pray for
    you in this regard?

6. How about the Psalm 119 **Digging Deeper**
    reading plan? Anything interesting there?

7. How can we support one another this week?
    Prayer requests? Praise reports?

Notes

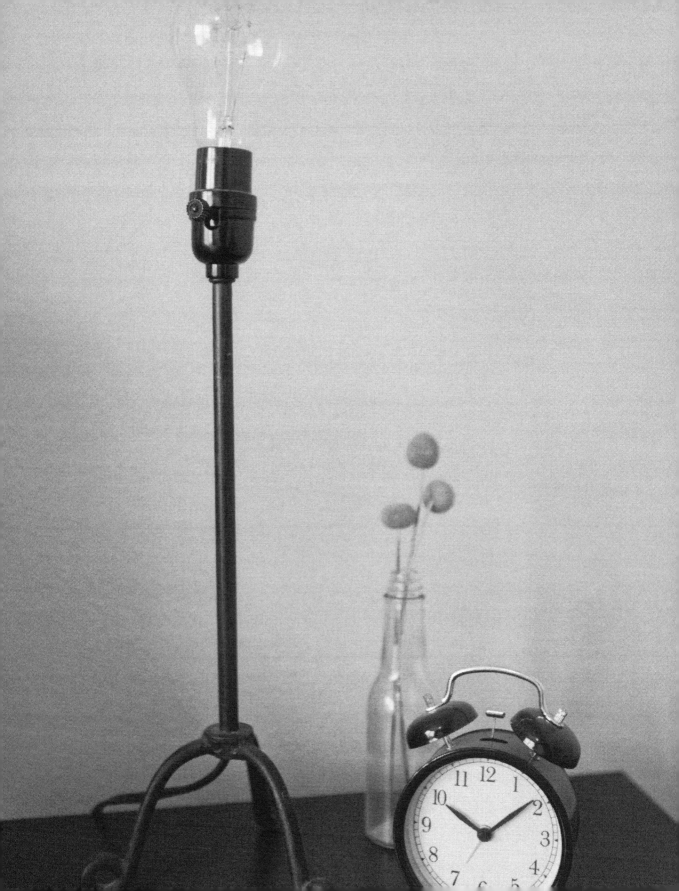

Wisdom in the Word

DECLARATION VERSE

"The unfolding of your words gives light;
it gives understanding to the simple."
Psalm 119:130

The Unfolding

"The unfolding of your words gives light; it gives understanding to the simple." Psalm 119:130

When I encounter Scripture I don't fully understand, I like to allow it time to roll over and over in my heart and mind. I savor its unique prose, meditate on its words, question its meaning.

What does it mean to unfold your words, God? How do your words bring light and give understanding?

As I pondered these questions and set them before the Lord, He reminded me of a story. My daughter was born with a neural tube defect. When the midwives discovered the abnormality, chaos and confusion filled the small room as they figured out what to do.

I lay in bed with what I thought was a perfectly healthy baby, only to be told: *"Your baby girl may never walk or function normally."*

Before these frightening words unfolded from the mouth of the attending doctor, the Lord had spoken His own Words to me. I wish I could say His Words were poetic and eloquent, but they were simply what my soul needed at that moment. The Lord said, *"Jenny, everything will be alright. Trust me."*

As the words from doctors, nurses, and test results continued to unfold all around me, they ricocheted off the only words that mattered: **The Word Himself.**

At that moment, when God spoke to my heart, I encountered the Word as my shelter in a storm of uncertainty. It illuminated the light of peace into the darkness. Fear fled at the sound of the Word.

> *"In the beginning was the Word, and the Word was with God, and the Word was God."* John 1:1

My second favorite thing to do as I encounter Scripture is to study the words used. I was intrigued by the word "light" used in Psalm 119:130. This word in its Hebrew translation means ***to illuminate, to become bright, to shine.*** When we encounter God's Word, it illuminates that which He is speaking. It shines the spotlight and makes brighter that which we cannot see.

The reality of life and of what we see in the natural can often leave our souls in the dark. Our mind, and even our words begin to wander, trying to grapple and understand what is going on around us.

My daughter spent her first night in the NICU while I sat on a cold, hard rocking chair. Although I had the support of my family and the prayers of my church, I was a single mom, and so I sat alone through the midnight hours. Answers were few, and understanding was limited, but I gripped tightly to what I had received only hours before.

The Word.

The light of the Word illuminated in the dark places of my soul and brought an understanding to the deepest places of my heart. I knew everything would, in fact, be alright—just as the Word had spoken.

I wish I could say that I go through life with the famous Bob Marley song *"Everything is going to be alright"* as my anthem when life doesn't go as I planned. Although, I trust in God's plans, timing, and goodness. I often struggle with the desire to grasp for a well-laid out blueprint to guide exactly how things will turn out. I want to know the details. I want to be in control!

Through this season of my life, the Lord reminded me of this: **when we encounter God as the Word, we don't need the details**. We don't need control. His words unfold in our hearts and in our minds, and we can't quite understand it, but everything begins to make sense. Our thoughts are in the proper place, our heart is at peace, and that which we couldn't see becomes clear before us.

We may not have answers, we may still question what is going on, but deep inside us, we know that it will be alright.

That God is who He says He is.

That He is walking with us and has good plans for us. That He can be trusted.

Have you experienced this kind of peace? The peace that surpasses an earthly understanding. (Philippians 4:7) The peace that seeps down into your soul and sits with you no matter the chaos and confusion around you?

When we encounter God, and the unfolding of His words, we experience supernatural peace. When we meditate on His words and speak them out, we encounter Him—the Author of the Word.

While I was pregnant with my daughter, a good friend gave me a very special book. Far better than *What to Expect When You're Expecting*, this book was about spiritually preparing our hearts and our bodies for the labor and delivery process. It compelled me to create a "birth plan" that included dozens of Scriptures that would be spoken over me while I was in the thick of laboring.

These words were rich in the atmosphere during the hours of laboring. They were alive and active in my heart and in my mind. ***Every time we declare Scripture, we are encountering the Word Himself.***

Hours later I would birth my sweet baby girl, and shortly thereafter as the words of confusion and chaos began to rise into the atmosphere, they couldn't help but clash against the words already spoken. ***The Word himself had taken up residence and shone a light.*** It helped me see through the smoke of fear quickly filling the room; it brought understanding and peace to my soul.

Ladies, be encouraged that the Bible is alive and active. (Hebrews 4:12) The Spirit of God lives in the Words of His story. When our voice gives breath to the Scriptures, they unfold before us, and we encounter the Lord God Himself.

And when we encounter God's promises, they shine a holy light that infuses our circumstances with truth. This allows us to walk one more step down the broken cobblestone road of our lives, and confidently say, *"Don't worry about a thing, because every little thing will be alright."*

Engage Prayer Method

The DECLARE Bible Study Approach begins by engaging or tuning your ears and heart to God's voice. The ENGAGE Prayer Method prepares your heart and mind to hear:

TOSS: Throw your cares on God. Let Him bear your burdens. *Psalm 55:22*

CATCH: Receive the peace that surpasses all understanding. *Philippians 4:7*

INVITE: Take every thought captive. Invite clarity and focus. Refuse confusion, distraction, or double-mindedness. *2 Corinthians 10:5*

OPEN: Ask God if you have turned away or closed your heart to anyone. Release the offense, open your heart, and give the situation into God's care. *Psalm 139:23*

EXPECT: Tell God that you are looking forward to hearing from Him. Let the excitement of time in His presence build expectation in your heart. *Habakkuk 2:1*

Wisdom in the Word

DAY ONE

Declaration Verse
"The unfolding of your words gives light;
it gives understanding to the simple."
Psalm 119:130

 **TODAY'S DECLARE PRACTICE** *Read & Write*

[ ] Read Psalm 119:130 slowly once or twice, out loud if you
   are able.

[ ] Write Psalm 119:129-131 in the space below. *Feel free to
   get creative!*

HAVE A LITTLE MORE TIME?

[ ] Read Psalm chapters 116 and 122 for context. Write out a
few observations.

_____

_____

_____

_____

_____

_____

[ ] Read Psalm 119:130 in another Bible translation.
Make note of the similarities and differences you see.

_____

_____

_____

_____

_____

_____

DIGGING DEEPER: PSALM 119:89-98

[ ] Read Psalm 119:89-98

[ ] Read and Write

Write any verse that stands out to you as you read
the passage.

[ ] Write any general thoughts or questions you have as you
read these verses.

Wisdom in
the Word

DAY TWO

Declaration Verse
Psalm 119:130

 TODAY'S DECLARE PRACTICE *Investigate*

Today we begin looking deeper into the Declaration Verse.
Investigate as little or as much as time allows. Online
resources like BibleGateway.com or BlueLetterBible.org
will help you during your investigation.

[ ] Conduct a Word Study: Part One

Read the Declaration Verse and highlight any words you
want to research more. Write these words below.

_____

_____

_____

_____

_____

_____

_____

_____

_____

[ ] Conduct a Word Study: Part Two

Using BlueLetterBible.org or another online resource,
choose a word you selected above to conduct your word
study. This is as simple as looking up the original Greek
or Hebrew word, reading the definitions of that word, and
looking at how it is used in other verses in the Bible.

Record the results of your word study here:

_____

_____

_____

_____

_____

_____

_____

HAVE A LITTLE MORE TIME?

[ ] Read these cross references for Psalm 119:130:

† Psalm 19:7

† Proverbs 6:23

† Acts 26:17-18

Reading cross references will help you better understand a verse, word, or principle.

What did you discover? Write your insights.

_____

_____

_____

_____

_____

_____

_____

[ ] Read a commentary. A commentary is a collection of explanatory notes written by a Bible scholar to help us understand the Scriptures. You can find these online. A good place to begin is Matthew Henry, C.H. Spurgeon, or David Guzik.

Write any observations, quotes, or notes.

_____

_____

_____

_____

_____

_____

_____

_____

DIGGING DEEPER: PSALM 119:99-108

[ ] Read Psalm 119:99-108

[ ] Investigate

Highlight a couple of key words that stand out to you in the verses you read. Using BlueLetterBible.org look up the Greek or Hebrew word and definition of one of those words.

Write your findings below.

_____

_____

_____

[ ] Write any general thoughts or questions you have as you
read the verses today.

Declaration Verse
Psalm 119:130

DAY THREE

 TODAY'S DECLARE PRACTICE *Imagine*

Remember to ENGAGE as you prepare to imagine: toss, catch, invite, open, expect. Invite the Word to speak personally into your mind and heart.

[ ] Read Psalm 119:130

Use your imagination and all your senses to be present in the scene.

[ ] How do God's words unfold or open? How does that look, sound, or feel?

_____

_____

_____

_____

_____

_____

_____

_____

_____

_____

[ ] Think about the beauty and warmth of light. How do God's words give light? What effect does that have in my life?

_____

_____

_____

_____

_____

_____

[ ] Do I need God's words for understanding, or can I find it elsewhere?

HAVE A LITTLE MORE TIME?

[ ] What characteristics of God are revealed in the Declaration Verse or chapter?

Is He steadfast, faithful, just, trustworthy, nurturing, kind, gentle, or strong? What do you see revealed about His nature in this passage of Scripture?

[ ] What promises of God are revealed in the Declaration Verse or chapter?

Write any observations, key words, or questions you have as you ponder the Declaration Verse. If you have time, you may want to do another word study

_____

_____

_____

_____

_____

_____

DIGGING DEEPER: PSALM 119:109-118

[ ] Read Psalm 119:109-118

[ ] Imagine

Imagine yourself in the scene as you ponder the following questions. What is happening? Imagine you are there. What do you notice?

_____

_____

[ ] Write any general thoughts or questions you have as you
    read the verses today.

Declaration Verse
Psalm 119:130

DAY FOUR

TODAY'S DECLARE PRACTICE *Listen*

Remember to ENGAGE as you prepare to listen: toss, catch, invite, open, expect. Invite the Word to speak personally into your mind and heart. God's voice will never accuse you. He may bring gentle conviction which can cause grief, but God always brings hope.

Listening can be pursued for several days. God may speak unexpectedly at random times of day or night as His revelation is released to you. Ask this question as you listen to God's voice:

[ ] How does this verse shine the light in my life?

_____

_____

_____

_____

 ## HAVE A LITTLE MORE TIME?

[ ] Ponder and pray: Dear Lord, my default is to trust in
my own understanding. Or if I'm not confident in myself,
I trust in other people. How would my problem-solving
process look different if I sought understanding in your
Word?

_____

_____

_____

_____

_____

DIGGING DEEPER: PSALM 119:119-126

[ ] Read Psalm 119:119-126

[ ] Listen

Ask yourself: how do these verses apply to me? Does God want to speak to my heart today through this passage?

_____

_____

_____

_____

_____

[ ] Write any general thoughts or questions you have as you read the verses today.

_____

_____

_____

_____

_____

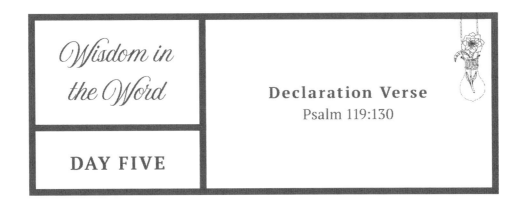

Wisdom in the Word

DAY FIVE

Declaration Verse
Psalm 119:130

 TODAY'S DECLARE PRACTICE *Declare*

Write a declaration of what you received as you meditated
on the Word. This can be a statement of God's promise
to you, an affirmation of the healing He has given you,
or a proclamation of a truth. A declaration may include
Scripture, your own words, or some of each.

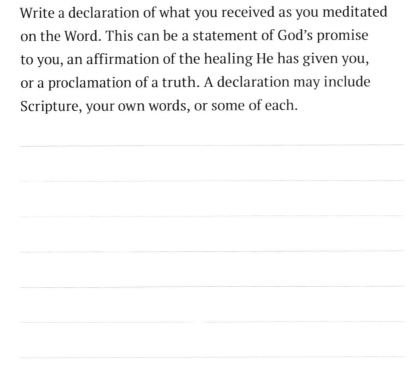

DIGGING DEEPER: PSALM 119:127-136

[ ] Read Psalm 119:127-136

[ ] Write any notes or observations as you read the verses today. Is there one verse that stands out to you?

_____

_____

_____

_____

[ ] How does this passage inspire you to walk in the light?

_____

_____

_____

_____

_____

_____

REFLECT ON YOUR WEEK 📅

Write out Psalm 119:130 by hand if you memorized it or summarize the Declaration Verse in your own words below.

_____

_____

_____

_____

_____

Spend a few minutes documenting your insights, "a-ha" moments, and revelations from this week of digging into the Bible.

_____

_____

_____

_____

_____

_____

_____

Week Three: Discussion Topics

We provide discussion topics to help facilitate conversations with friends as you enjoy this study together, or you can ponder these questions as a personal reflection. Even if you are not able to meet up with others, you're invited to join us in our private Facebook Group at facebook.com/groups/flourishgathering/

1. Do you have any thoughts or reactions to this week's devotional? Here are two passages from *The Unfolding* to inspire conversation:

   "The reality of life and of what we see in the natural can often leave our souls in the dark. Our mind, and even our words begin to wander trying to grapple and find understanding to what is going on around us." (page 84)

   "Through this season of my life, the Lord reminded me of this: when we encounter God as the Word, we don't need the details. We don't need control. His words unfold in our hearts and in our minds, and we can't quite understand it, but everything begins to make sense. Our thoughts are in the proper place, our heart is at peace, and that which we couldn't see becomes clear before us." (page 85)

2. Was there a special insight you gained from the **Investigate** practice? Perhaps an interesting word study, cross reference, or commentary?

3. What happened when you used your **Imagination**? What did you discover about the context of this chapter or book of the Bible? If you had time, did you gain insight into the character or promises of God?

4. Did God speak something special that you would like to share as you **Listened**?

5. What is your **Declaration**? How can we pray for you in this regard?

6. How about the Psalm 119 **Digging Deeper** reading plan? Anything interesting there?

7. How can we support one another this week? Prayer requests? Praise reports?

Notes

_____

_____

_____

_____

_____

_____

_____

_____

_____

_____

_____

_____

_____

_____

_____

_____

Love the Word

DECLARATION VERSE

"Great peace have those who love your law,
and nothing can make them stumble."
Psalm 119:165

Tame This Wayward Heart

My burden was anything but light. My yoke was not at all easy. I stumbled under the weight of sin, distant from God. I had chosen to go my own way, against the advice of Scripture, defying all I knew to be true and noble and lovely.

I yielded to temptation and reached for the apple.

With the succulent juice of sin glistening on my lips, and my tongue savoring the deliciousness, I knew the pleasure would not last. Sin swallowed makes a stomach sick.

I argued with my conscience. What a burden to know the truth. Why couldn't I sin like everyone else, blissfully unaware of the deadly consequences?

It wasn't fair! I longed to indulge my flesh, to snatch the forbidden fruit and feast gluttonously until my belly bulged, satisfied by hedonism.

Other people seem happy in their trespasses. They enjoy all manner of elicit indulgences, reveling until dawn, embraced by countless lovers. I wished to be so carefree and self-gratifying; however, when I chose sin, the garden of my heart became overrun by thorns and thistles, destroying the tranquility I once enjoyed.

Crushed by the burden of walking in darkness, I wiped my mouth, spit out the apple, and cried for help, *"Jesus, please, forgive me."*

> *"Surely the arm of the Lord is not too short to save,*
> *nor his ear too dull to hear. But your iniquities have*
> *separated you from your God; your sins have hidden his*
> *face from you, so that he will not hear."* Isaiah 59:1-2

Repentance drew me to my Father's embrace, gazing into His eyes, hearing His voice. Jesus' blood cleansed me from guilt and shame and strengthened me to repent to those I harmed by my sinful actions. I felt the weight of my iniquities lift from my shoulders as I received forgiveness and clung to His love.

I returned to the Word of God, the love story that shows me how to walk in the light. My stumbling feet found steady ground. Holy Spirit cleared the brambles from the path as torment gave way to calm.

> *"Great peace have those who love your law, and nothing can*
> *make them stumble."* Psalm 119:165

When peace displaces anxiety or hardness of heart, the contrast is breathtaking. Sweet fellowship with my Abba Father made me believe that I would hold fast to God's law forever. How could sin ever entice me again? It's dreadful.

I have found that humility makes me alert and sober, attuned to God's voice, able to discern the enemy's plans. Humility keeps me dependent on Christ, obedient to Him.

The psalmist affirms his love for the law and his desire to obey God's precepts. He chief desire is to heed God's instructions, to follow His directions, to abide by His counsel.

Why do I sense an undercurrent of discomfort? My proud rebellious heart bristles. I reflexively resist when others require me to comply. I want to decide for myself, to choose the way that is right in my own eyes.

Oh, to tame this wayward heart!

> *Let Thy goodness, like a fetter, Bind my wandering heart to Thee. Prone to wander, Lord, I feel it, Prone to leave the God I love; Here's my heart, O take and seal it, Seal it for Thy courts above.* (Robert Robinson, Come Thou Fount of Every Blessing, 1757)

With the message of Psalm 119 shining a light on our steps, we recognize that **the Word of God holds us close in the protective glow of His love.** Jesus knows we are fickle, distracted by fleshly desires, prone to idolize worldly treasures. Because we cannot save ourselves, He came to earth and sacrificed Himself to free us from the stronghold of iniquity.

All He asks is that we stay near to Him, nourished by His Word, rejecting the sin that so easily entangles. (Hebrews 12:1) He does not ask us to do this in our own strength. We are not able. But He is.

"Are you tired? Worn out? Burned out on religion? Come to me. Get away with me and you'll recover your life. I'll show you how to take a real rest. Walk with me and work with me—watch how I do it. Learn the unforced rhythms of grace. I won't lay anything heavy or ill-fitting on you. Keep company with me and you'll learn to live freely and lightly." Matthew 11:28-30 (MSG)

When we keep in step with Jesus and obey His instruction, we reap supernatural joy and unexpected peace. **All we need to do is love Him first and love Him more.** *Even more than that forbidden fruit.* Don't be fooled. Once you've walked in the light, nothing else will satisfy. Live freely and lightly. Yes, that is our desire.

Engage Prayer Method

The DECLARE Bible Study Approach begins by engaging or tuning your ears and heart to God's voice. The ENGAGE Prayer Method prepares your heart and mind to hear:

TOSS: Throw your cares on God. Let Him bear your burdens. *Psalm 55:22*

CATCH: Receive the peace that surpasses all understanding. *Philippians 4:7*

INVITE: Take every thought captive. Invite clarity and focus. Refuse confusion, distraction, or double-mindedness. *2 Corinthians 10:5*

OPEN: Ask God if you have turned away or closed your heart to anyone. Release the offense, open your heart, and give the situation into God's care. *Psalm 139:23*

EXPECT: Tell God that you are looking forward to hearing from Him. Let the excitement of time in His presence build expectation in your heart. *Habakkuk 2:1*

Love the Word

DAY ONE

Declaration Verse

"Great peace have those who love your law, and nothing can make them stumble."
Psalm 119:165

 **TODAY'S DECLARE PRACTICE** *Read & Write*

[ ] Read Psalm 119:165 slowly once or twice, out loud if you are able.

[ ] Write Psalm 119:164-66 in the space below. *Feel free to get creative!*

HAVE A LITTLE MORE TIME?

[ ] Read Psalm Chapters 115 and 123 for context. Write out a few observations:

_____

_____

_____

_____

_____

_____

[ ] Read Psalm 119:165 in another Bible translation. Make note of the similarities and differences you see.

_____

_____

_____

_____

_____

_____

DIGGING DEEPER: PSALM 119:137-144

[ ] Read Psalm 119:137-144

[ ] Read and Write

Write any verse that stands out to you as you read the passage.

_____

_____

_____

_____

_____

[ ] Write any general thoughts or questions you have as you
read the verses today.

_____

_____

_____

_____

_____

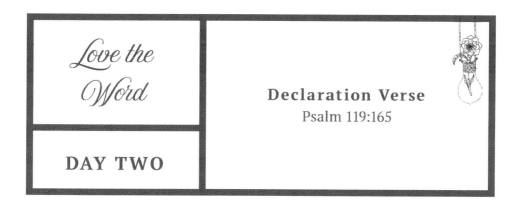

Love the Word

DAY TWO

Declaration Verse
Psalm 119:165

 TODAY'S DECLARE PRACTICE *Investigate*

Today we begin looking deeper into the Declaration Verse.
Investigate as little or as much as time allows. Online
resources like BibleGateway.com or BlueLetterBible.org
will help you during your investigation.

[ ] Conduct a Word Study: Part One

Read the Declaration Verse and highlight any words you want
to research more. Write these words below.

_____

_____

_____

_____

[ ] Conduct a Word Study: Part Two

Using BlueLetterBible.org or another online resource, choose a word you selected above to conduct your word study. This is as simple as looking up the original Greek or Hebrew word, reading the definitions of that word, and looking at how it is used in other verses in the Bible.

Record the results of your word study here.

_____

_____

_____

_____

_____

_____

_____

 HAVE A LITTLE MORE TIME?

[ ] Read these cross references for Psalm 119:165:

    †   Proverbs 3:1-2

    †   Philippians 4:6-7

    †   Isaiah 48:17-18

Reading cross references will help you better understand a verse, word, or principle. What did you discover? Write your insights.

[ ] Read a commentary. A commentary is a collection of explanatory notes written by a Bible scholar to help us understand the Scriptures. You can find these online. A good place to begin is Matthew Henry, C.H. Spurgeon, or David Guzik,

Write any observations, quotes, or notes.

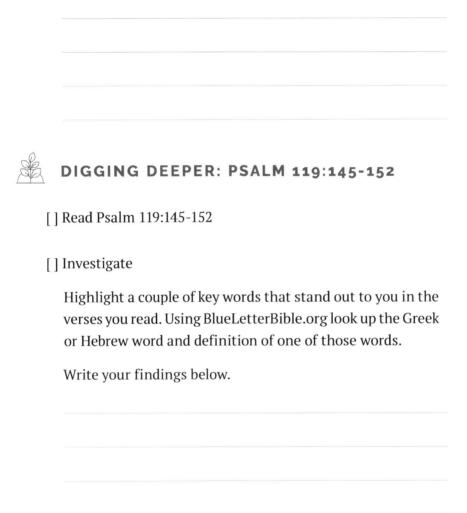

DIGGING DEEPER: PSALM 119:145-152

[ ] Read Psalm 119:145-152

[ ] Investigate

Highlight a couple of key words that stand out to you in the verses you read. Using BlueLetterBible.org look up the Greek or Hebrew word and definition of one of those words.

Write your findings below.

[ ] Write any general thoughts or questions you have as you
     read the verses today.

Declaration Verse
Psalm 119:165

DAY THREE

 TODAY'S DECLARE PRACTICE *Imagine*

> *Remember to take a moment to Engage as you prepare to imagine: toss, catch, invite, open, expect. Invite the Word to speak personally into your mind and heart.*

[ ] Read Psalm 119:165

Use your imagination and all your senses to be present in the scene.

[ ] What would be different in my life if I had great peace?

_____

_____

_____

_____

_____

_____

_____

[ ] I want to love your Word more, God, please teach me how.
What is holding me back?

_____

_____

_____

_____

_____

[ ] How does your Word keep me from stumbling? What does
that look like?

_____

_____

_____

_____

_____

_____

_____

_____

_____

_____

_____

HAVE A LITTLE MORE TIME?

[ ] What characteristics of God are revealed in the Declaration Verse or chapter?

Is He steadfast, faithful, just, trustworthy, nurturing, kind, gentle, or strong? What do you see revealed about His nature in this passage of Scripture?

_____

_____

_____

_____

_____

_____

_____

_____

_____

_____

_____

_____

_____

[ ] What promises of God are revealed in the Declaration
Verse?

Write any observations, key words, or questions you have
as you ponder the Declaration Verse. If you have time, you
may want to do another word study.

_____

_____

_____

_____

_____

_____

_____

DIGGING DEEPER: PSALM 119:153-160

[ ] Read Psalm 119:153-160

[ ] Imagine

Insert yourself in the scene as you ponder the following
questions. What is happening? Imagine you are there.
What do you notice?

_____

_____

_____

_____

[ ] Write any general thoughts or questions you have as you
read the passage today.

_____

_____

_____

_____

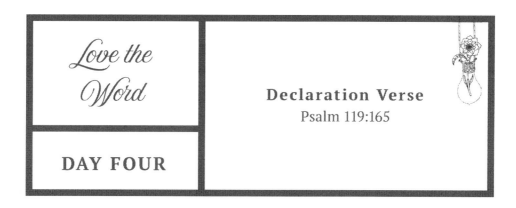

Love the
Word

DAY FOUR

Declaration Verse
Psalm 119:165

 TODAY'S DECLARE PRACTICE

Remember to ENGAGE as you prepare to listen: toss, catch, invite, open, expect. Invite the Word to speak personally into your mind and heart. God's voice will never accuse you. He may bring gentle conviction which can cause grief, but God always brings hope.

Listening can be pursued for several days. God may speak unexpectedly at random times of day or night as His revelation is released to you. Ask these questions as you listen to God's voice:

[ ] How can I walk with confidence in your promises?

_____

_____

_____

_____

_____

_____

_____

🌱 HAVE A LITTLE MORE TIME?

[ ] Ponder and pray: What needs to shift in my heart and
mind so I can love your Word even more?

_____

_____

_____

_____

_____

_____

DIGGING DEEPER: PSALM 119:161-168

[ ] Read Psalm 119:161-168

[ ] Listen

Ask yourself: how does what I have read so far in Psalm 119 apply to me? What does God want to speak to me through these verses?

_____

_____

_____

_____

_____

[ ] Write any general thoughts or questions you have as you read the passage.

_____

_____

_____

_____

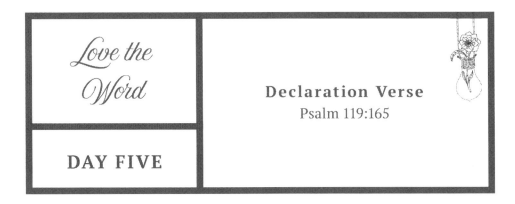

Love the Word

DAY FIVE

Declaration Verse
Psalm 119:165

TODAY'S DECLARE PRACTICE *Declare*

Write out a declaration of what you received as you
meditated on the Word. This can be a statement of
God's promise to you, an affirmation of the healing He
has given you, or a proclamation of a truth. A declaration
may include Scripture, your own words, or some of each.

_____

_____

_____

_____

_____

_____

_____

_____

_____

DIGGING DEEPER: PSALM 119:169-176

[ ] Read Psalm 119:169-176

[ ] Write any notes or observations as you read the verses
today. Is there one verse that stands out to you?

_____

_____

_____

_____

[ ] How does this passage inspire you to walk in the light?

_____

_____

_____

_____

REFLECT ON YOUR WEEK 📅

Write out Psalm 119:165 by hand if you memorized it or
summarize the Declaration Verse in your own words below.

_____

_____

_____

_____

_____

_____

Spend a few minutes documenting your insights, "a-ha"
moments, and revelations from this week of digging into
the Bible.

_____

_____

_____

_____

_____

_____

_____

Week Four: Discussion Topics

We provide discussion topics to help facilitate conversations with friends as you enjoy this study together, or you can ponder these questions as a personal reflection. Even if you are not able to meet up with others, you're invited to join us in our private Facebook Group at facebook.com/groups/flourishgathering/

1. Do you have any thoughts or reactions to this week's devotional? Here are two passages from *Tame this Wayward Heart* to inspire conversation:

   "I returned to the Word of God, the love story that shows me how to walk in the light. My stumbling feet found steady ground. Holy Spirit cleared the brambles from the path as torment gave way to calm. When peace displaces anxiety or hardness of heart, the contrast is breathtaking." (page 114)

   "The Word of God holds us close in the protective glow of His love. Jesus knows we are fickle, distracted by fleshly desires, prone to idolize worldly treasures. Because we cannot save ourselves, He came to earth and sacrificed Himself to free us from the stronghold of iniquity." (page 115)

2. Was there a special insight you gained from the
    Investigate practice? Perhaps an interesting
    word study, cross reference, or commentary?

3. What happened when you used your **Imagination**?
    What did you discover about the context of
    this chapter or book of the Bible? If you had
    time, did you gain insight into the character or
    promises of God?

4. Did God speak something special that you would
    like to share as you **Listened**?

5. What is your **Declaration**? How can we pray for
    you in this regard?

6. How about the Psalm 119 **Digging Deeper**
    reading plan? Anything interesting there?

7. How can we support one another this week?
    Prayer requests? Praise reports?

Notes

The conclusion of a Flourish Study imparts a bitter-sweet feeling. In God's kindness, He creates this space and invites us to enjoy time with Him in the pages of this journal and in our community of women. He is present in our devotion. He speaks into our lives and fills up our hearts with His love. The Lord, whose holy name is the very breath in our bodies, loves to spend time with His daughters and shine His light onto our path.

When we walk in the light of God's Word, we begin to see the heights and depths like never before. We embark on a life-long treasure hunt, seeking out the mysteries, yearning for revelation to keep us on the path of life.

We pray that you will become increasingly curious about the Scriptures and continue using the DECLARE Bible Study Approach for yourself. Complex questions are opened in the Word that inspire a lifetime of exploration. We crack open a door to the Word of God so that you learn to enjoy studying and investigating for the rest of your life. Don't stay away for long. Read and ponder and pray. Come back to the Word time and time again as the circumstances of your life shift and ask God what He wishes to reveal at each crossroads that you face.

No matter the circumstances in your life, we pray that the message revealed by Holy Spirit will make clear the Lord's path for you. You will not always find easy answers, but instead the Scriptures will point you to the only One who can answer. Enjoy the journey as you walk in the light of God's Word.

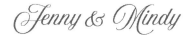

A little bit about Flourish

Flourish is a gathering of women who passionately pursue God and His Word. We encourage one another through genuine, transparent relationships which equip us to thrive where we are planted and impact our world for the glory of God.

We believe that the power of God's Word revealed by the Spirit changes lives. In relationship with God and with one another, we are strengthened to overcome hindrances in our journey. Flourish is dedicated to bringing God's Word to life in the 21st Century by encouraging women that the Word is alive, active, and powerful today.

Now here's our purpose spelled out in regular talk.

We want more of God, so we dig into His Word. We can't survive without Him. We can't survive without you either. You can leave your mask at the door because real life is messy, and no one here is pretending to have it all together

At Flourish we...

ENCOURAGE

We share real stories of real life with transparency and honesty, always pointing to the promises found in God's Word.

EQUIP

Flourish provides tools and resources that are grounded in the Word of God. Our community provides a safe place to learn and to grow.

ACTIVATE

We seek God in community because, when the rubber hits the road, we want to see evidence of God's life in our relationships.

About the Authors

Meet Mindy. . .

Mindy Kiker is a committed Floridian, enjoying a quiet wood-land home that she and her husband built to shelter their four boisterous boys. Born in Tucson, Arizona, Mindy's magical childhood included a four-year hiatus on the big island of Hawaii where she danced the hula, and later helped with the family marina in Cedar Key where she learned to cast net and sail the Gulf of Mexico. The Kikers spent the 1990s in South Africa, returning with their brood for a sabbatical year in 2012 to reconnect with beloved friends and favorite places.

Now that Mindy's spring-chicken days are drawing to a close, she has accepted her role as an "older" woman (it's all relative) cheering others on in life's journey. A favorite verse that motivates her to keep pressing into God and encouraging her friends to do the same is *Galatians 5:1, "It is for freedom that Christ has set us free. Stand firm, then, and do not let yourselves be burdened again by a yoke of slavery."*

And Jenny. . .

Jenny Kochert was born and raised in sunny South Florida. Although she took full advantage of big-city life growing up, she longed to move to a quieter town, and college provided the perfect excuse! After graduating from the University of Florida, Jenny followed in the family footsteps and became a private investigator (yes, you read that right!), opening her own agency in 2005.

However, once she became a mom to her daughter, Sophia, she turned in her badge, and settled at home, now home schooling her daughter. Jenny, her husband Ryan, and daughter Sophia now live in Northern Kentucky where they serve in ministry together as a family. God has put a story on her lips and a passion in her heart to encourage women, and she is thrilled that she gets to do that each and every day.

Other Flourish Studies you may enjoy

THIS IS HIS STORY:
THE POWER OF GOD
REVEALED IN YOUR LIFE

What story do you want your life to tell?

The sun rises on a new scene in your story every day. Your relationships, words, and thoughts propel the plot and action forward to an unknown future. In some seasons, you face significant trials or crossroads, while others are filled with daily obligations and responsibilities.

You want to create a story you're proud to live, but it's hard to know how. Doubt steals your confidence. Fear attacks your joy. You strain to hear the still, small voice, but the message is unclear. *I hope I'm on the right path, but how can I be sure?*

When you stand on the Word of God, your path comes into focus. Your story becomes a God Story empowered by faith, courage and perseverance. *Sounds promising, but how do I get there?*

We are inspired by the life of Gideon, trapped in a bleak period of Israel's history. Burdened by poverty and oppression, he accused God of abandonment. But God had a rescue plan ready. Gideon was an unlikely recruit to lead his people. Despite self-doubt and fear, he found the faith and endurance to press through to victory.

Gideon's story of courage is revealed in **This is His Story**, a 20-day self-paced Bible study journal that guides you step-by-step using the DECLARE Bible Study Approach. This less-is-more approach invites you to dig into the Word and hear God speak.

Join us to discover how the surpassing greatness of God's power shows up in the story of your life.

FEASTING ON GOD'S WORD

Are you feeling spiritually weary and hungry for more of God's Word? Do you desire to learn how to dig into Scripture for yourself?

You are invited to join us at the feasting table! Satisfy your soul as you slow down and savor God's Word. Pull up a chair to the table bountiful with spiritual nourishment.

Let's experience how the daily bread of God's Word and the living water of His truths can satisfy even the most famished spirit.

Feasting on God's Word is a 20-day self-paced Bible study journal that guides you step-by-step as you study four key Scriptures using the DECLARE Bible Study Approach. This less-is-more approach guides you to dig into the Bible and hear God speak as you learn to apply five simple daily practices: read & write, investigate, imagine, listen and declare the Word.

As you are **Feasting on God's Word**, you will explore the story of Job who holds fast to the Word of the Lord as if life depends on it. You will discover that perseverance ignites the sustaining power of God's Word, even in the face of unspeakable loss. How can you, like this faithful follower, endure hardship and yet remain steadfast?

Jesus extends a personal invitation for each of us to receive and be filled with His Word just like the prophet Jeremiah who describes his appetite for the presence of the Lord: *"When your words came, I ate them; they were my joy and my heart's delight, for I bear your name, Lord God Almighty." Jeremiah 15:16*

Join us as we feast on God's Word. Your place at the table awaits.

Thank you

For Flourishing with Us!

Connect with us on Facebook
@Flourishgathering
@Flourishwriters

†

Contact us
info@flourishgathering.com

†

Visit us
Flourishgathering.com
Flourishwriters.com

Made in the USA
Middletown, DE
02 September 2019